This Book Belongs To:

COPYRIGHT © 2004 Nanci Bell
Gander Publishing
P.O. Box 780, 450 Front Street
Avila Beach, CA 93424
805-541-5523 • 800-554-1819

17   16   15   14   4   5   6   7

ISBN 0-945856-45-8   978-0-945856-45-0

4-140306

Overview and Directions

This workbook is designed to develop gestalt imagery and language comprehension with the *Visualizing and Verbalizing for Language Comprehension and Thinking*® (V/V®) program.

Following the steps of V/V, detail and gestalt imagery are developed with Sentence by Sentence, Multiple Sentence, Whole Paragraph, and Paragraph by Paragraph V/V stimulation.

Each story is high in imagery and followed by these workbook activities:

- Imagery Questions
- Picture Summary
- Word Summary
- Main Idea
- Higher Order Thinking (HOT) Questions
- Paragraph Writing

As the student begins each story, he/she should decode the vocabulary words and visualize the meaning. This will help create imagery and develop contextual fluency. The student may write phrases or partial sentences to describe his/her imagery.

These workbooks have been written specifically to help students learn and discover the wonder of the written word by improving gestalt imagery, critical thinking, and writing skills. Once these skills are developed, the possibilities are endless.

Remember, you can help students do this. You can do anything!

Nanci Bell
2004

There are three workbooks at each reading level:

Book A • Sentence by Sentence
Book B • Sentence by Sentence and Multiple Sentence
Book C • Multiple Sentence, Whole Paragraph, and Paragraph by Paragraph

---

To all
the imagery
waiting
to be
awakened

1 A Living Teddy Bear

The gray and white koala lives in the tall eucalyptus tree where she eats the leaves for food and drink. She has a big rubbery nose and large round, fluffy ears that make her look like a teddy bear. She grips the tree trunk tightly with her sharp claws and climbs around picking leaves at night. On cold days, she sleeps in the branches, curled up in a ball with her soft thick fur helping to keep her warm. On hot days, she sleeps with her legs dangled over a branch in an effort to cool off.

Vocabulary to Visualize:

koala: a small furry animal from Australia
eucalyptus: a tall tree from Australia
dangled: hung down; swung freely

---

1 **First Sentence:** The gray and white koala lives in the tall eucalyptus tree where she eats the leaves for food and drink.

What did those words make you picture? _____

_____

_____

What did you picture for...

1. the koala? _____

_____

2. the eucalyptus tree? _____

_____

3. the leaves of the tree? _____

_____

4. the koala eating? _____

_____

---

2 **Second Sentence:** She has a big rubbery nose and large round, fluffy ears that make her look like a teddy bear.

What did those words make you picture? _____

_____

_____

What did you picture for...

1. her nose? _____

_____

2. her ears? _____

_____

3. "fluffy" ears? _____

_____

4. a teddy bear? _____

_____

3 **Third Sentence:** She grips the tree trunk tightly with her sharp claws and climbs around picking leaves at night.

What did those words make you picture? _____

_____

_____

What did you picture for...

1. the tree trunk? _____

_____

2. the koala's sharp claws? _____

_____

3. her climbing around? _____

_____

4. her picking leaves? _____

_____

4 **Fourth Sentence:** On cold days, she sleeps in the branches, curled up in a ball with her soft thick fur helping to keep her warm.

What did those words make you picture? _____

_____

_____

What did you picture for...

1. the branches of the tree? _____

_____

2. the koala sleeping? _____

_____

3. her curled up? _____

_____

4. her fur? _____

_____

5 **Fifth Sentence:** On hot days, she sleeps with her legs dangled over a branch in an effort to cool off.

What did those words make you picture? _____

_____

_____

What did you picture for...

1. hot days? _____

_____

2. the koala's legs dangling? _____

_____

3. her cooling off? _____

_____

Picture Summary:

Number your images in order.

[ ] The koala grips the tree trunk tightly, climbing around to pick leaves to eat.

[ ] The koala has lots of thick fur that helps keep her warm on cold days.

[ ] The koala uses the leaves of the eucalyptus tree for food and drink.

[ ] The koala dangles her legs over a tree branch on hot days to cool off.

Critical Thinking

Write a Word Summary:

_____

_____

_____

_____

_____

Main Idea:

Check the box that best describes all your images—the main idea.

☐ The gray and white koala looks like a teddy bear with her big fluffy ears and rubbery fur.

☐ The koala climbs around the eucalyptus tree with her very sharp claws gripping the tree trunk.

☐ The koala lives and sleeps in the eucalyptus tree, picking leaves at night, and sleeping in the branches during the day.

HOT Questions:

1. Why do you think it might be important for the koala to have sharp claws? _____

_____

2. Why do you think it is important for the koala to grip the trunk of the tree tightly? _____

_____

3. Why do you think it is important for the koala to have thick fur? _____

_____

4. Why do you think the eucalyptus tree is a great place for the koala to live? _____

_____

5. How might dangling her legs help keep her cool? _____

_____

6. Do you think koalas ever come down out of the trees? Why or why not? _____

_____

Make up a story about a koala bear in a tall eucalyptus tree during a great storm.

_____

_____

_____

_____

_____

_____

_____

_____

_____

_____

_____

_____

_____

_____

_____

_____

Did you use all of the Structure Words? Check each one you used.

| ☐ What | ☐ Number | ☐ Color | ☐ Mood | ☐ Background | ☐ Perspective |
| ☐ Size | ☐ Shape | ☐ Movement | ☐ Where | ☐ When | ☐ Sound |

2 Siegfried & Roy

Siegfried and Roy were flashy magicians who performed illusion tricks on stage at a grand hotel in Las Vegas. Set to exciting music and colorful fire displays, their show featured vanishing acts with rare white tigers. In one trick, they led a tame tiger into one of two empty metal cages raised far apart on stage. Then both cages were covered with white sheets as the audience waited breathlessly. When the sheets were lifted, the tiger had switched cages.

Vocabulary to Visualize:

magicians: performers who use tricks and illusions in their acts
illusion: something that looks real but isn't
Las Vegas: a city in the state of Nevada that is famous for its entertainment
vanishing: disappearing, no longer seen

---

1 **First Sentence:** Siegfried and Roy were flashy magicians who performed illusion tricks on stage at a grand hotel in Las Vegas.

What did those words make you picture? _____

_____

What did you picture for...

1. Siegfried and Roy? _____

2. "flashy magicians"? _____

3. them doing tricks on stage? _____

4. a grand hotel? _____

---

2 **Second Sentence:** Set to exciting music and colorful fire displays, their show featured vanishing acts with rare white tigers.

What did those words make you picture? _____

_____

What did you picture for...

1. their show? _____

2. the fire displays? _____

3. the white tigers? _____

4. the sound of the music? _____

3 **Third Sentence:** In one trick, they led a tame tiger into one of two empty metal cages raised far apart on stage.

What did those words make you picture?_____

_____

_____

What did you picture for...

1. a tame tiger? _____

_____

2. them leading the tiger? _____

_____

3. the two cages on stage? _____

_____

4. the tiger in one cage? _____

_____

4 **Fourth Sentence:** Then both cages were covered with white sheets as the audience waited breathlessly.

What did those words make you picture?_____

_____

_____

What did you picture for...

1. the sheets? _____

_____

2. the cages being covered?_____

_____

3. the audience? _____

_____

4. the sound of the audience waiting? _____

_____

5 **Fifth Sentence:** When the sheets were lifted, the tiger had switched cages.

What did those words make you picture? _____

_____

_____

What did you picture for...

1. the sheets being lifted? _____

_____

2. the cage where the tiger had been? _____

_____

3. where the tiger is now? _____

_____

Picture Summary:

Number your images in order.

☐ Both cages were covered with white sheets while the audience watched.

☐ The tame white tiger was led into one of the two cages.

☐ The magicians Siegfried and Roy performed illusion tricks on stage at a Las Vegas hotel.

☐ The sheets were lifted, showing the audience that the tiger had switched cages.

Write a Word Summary:

_____

_____

_____

_____

Main Idea:

Check the box that best describes all your images—the main idea.

☐ Siegfried and Roy performed magic tricks with white tigers on stage in a show in Las Vegas.

☐ The tame white tiger was led into one cage, covered, and then reappeared in a second cage.

☐ Siegfried and Roy perform flame displays on stage in a grand hotel in Las Vegas.

HOT Questions:

1. Why do you think Siegfried and Roy performed on stage? _____

_____

2. Why do you think their show was set to exciting music? _____

_____

3. Why do you think their show had flashy fire displays? _____

_____

4. Why do you think they had white tigers in their show? _____

_____

5. Why do you think it might be important that Siegfried and Roy use tame tigers instead of wild ones? _____

_____

6. How do you think they did the trick where the tiger moved from cage to cage? _____

_____

Make up a story about an exciting magic act.

_____

_____

_____

_____

_____

_____

_____

_____

_____

_____

_____

_____

_____

_____

_____

Did you use all of the Structure Words? Check each one you used.

☐ What	☐ Number	☐ Color	☐ Mood	☐ Background	☐ Perspective
☐ Size	☐ Shape	☐ Movement	☐ Where	☐ When	☐ Sound

3 Wildlife Painting

Thousands of years ago, men drew pictures on walls, deep inside caves, of the animals they saw each day. The earliest artists drew on the stone walls with charcoal and added colors made from bits of dirt and berries. They drew huge wooly mammoths with tusks like those they hunted. They sketched wild tigers and bears like those they ran and hid from. Fierce bulls and herds of graceful deer have been running across the cave walls for ages.

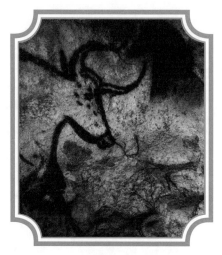

Vocabulary to Visualize:

charcoal: pieces of burnt wood that can be used to draw with
mammoths: extinct large hairy animals similar to elephants
tusks: long thick front teeth
ages: hundreds or thousands of years

---

1 **First Sentence:** Thousands of years ago, men drew pictures on walls, deep inside caves, of the animals they saw each day.

What did those words make you picture?_____

_____

_____

What did you picture for...

1. men drawing?_____

_____

2. the caves?_____

_____

3. the walls deep inside?_____

_____

4. the animals they drew?_____

_____

---

2 **Second Sentence:** The earliest artists drew on the stone walls with charcoal and added colors made from bits of dirt and berries.

What did those words make you picture?_____

_____

_____

What did you picture for...

1. the charcoal?_____

_____

2. the artists drawing with charcoal?_____

_____

3. the color of the dirt?_____

_____

4. the color of the berries?_____

3 **Third Sentence:** They drew huge wooly mammoths with tusks like those they hunted.

What did those words make you picture? _____

_____

What did you picture for...

1. the wooly mammoths they drew? _____

_____

2. the mammoths' size? _____

_____

3. their tusks? _____

_____

4. the men hunting them? _____

_____

4 **Fourth Sentence:** They sketched wild tigers and bears like those they ran and hid from.

What did those words make you picture? _____

_____

What did you picture for...

1. the tigers? _____

_____

2. the bears? _____

_____

3. the men running away? _____

_____

4. the men hiding? _____

_____

5 **Fifth Sentence:** Fierce bulls and herds of graceful deer have been running across the cave walls for ages.

What did those words make you picture? _____

_____

What did you picture for...

1. the bulls? _____

_____

2. the herds of deer? _____

_____

3. them "running across the cave walls"? _____

_____

Picture Summary:

Number your images in order.

☐ Bulls and herds of deer run across the cave walls.

☐ The early artists drew the animals they saw around them every day.

☐ They drew woolly mammoths, tigers, and bears.

☐ The drawings were made with charcoal on the walls of deep caves, and were colored with dirt or berries.

Critical Thinking

Write a Word Summary:

_____

_____

_____

_____

Main Idea:

Check the box that best describes all your images—the main idea.

☐ The huge wooly mammoth with big tusks lived thousands of years ago, and the earliest men hunted it.

☐ Early men drew pictures of animals on cave walls with charcoal and colored them with bits of dirt and berries.

☐ The earliest artists were men who painted wild tigers, wooly mammoths, deer, and bears on cave walls.

HOT Questions:

1. Why do you think the men drew on the walls of caves and not the floors?_____

_____

2. Why do you think it is important that the drawings were deep inside the caves?_____

_____

3. Why do you think they painted animals? _____

_____

4. Why do you think they made their colors from berries and dirt and not paint?_____

_____

5. Why might they sometimes draw animals they were afraid of? _____

_____

6. Why do you think these paintings might be important today?_____

_____

Make up a story about an artist drawing an exciting scene on a cave wall.

_____

_____

_____

_____

_____

_____

_____

_____

_____

_____

_____

_____

_____

_____

_____

_____

_____

Did you use all of the Structure Words? Check each one you used.

☐ What   ☐ Number   ☐ Color   ☐ Mood   ☐ Background   ☐ Perspective
☐ Size   ☐ Shape   ☐ Movement   ☐ Where   ☐ When   ☐ Sound

4 Acupuncture

Acupuncture is an ancient Chinese medical practice that uses needles to help relieve pain. The patient lies still on a table while thin metal needles are poked under his skin at points on his body. When the needles are in place, the patient may feel tingly or numb. After the needles are removed, he should feel relaxed and pain free. He may return for more sessions to help with his chronic pain and to keep him in good health.

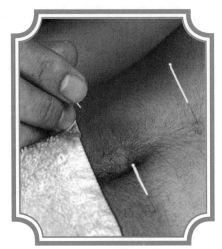

Vocabulary to Visualize:

acupuncture: a technique for relieving pain with needles
Chinese: of or from China, a large country in Asia
patient: a person who seeks medical help
chronic: constant, unrelenting

1
First Sentence: Acupuncture is an ancient Chinese medical practice that uses needles to help relieve pain.

What did those words make you picture?_____

_____

What did you picture for...

1. acupuncture?_____

2. an ancient medical practice?_____

3. it using needles?_____

4. pain? _____

2
Second Sentence: The patient lies still on a table while thin metal needles are poked under his skin at points on his body.

What did those words make you picture?_____

_____

What did you picture for...

1. the patient? _____

2. the patient lying still?_____

3. the table?_____

4. the needles in his skin? _____

3 **Third Sentence:** When the needles are in place, the patient may feel tingly or numb.

What did those words make you picture?_____

_____

What did you picture for...

1. where on his body the needles are? _____

_____

2. a tingly feeling? _____

3. a numb feeling? _____

4. where this is happening? _____

4 **Fourth Sentence:** After the needles are removed, he should feel relaxed and pain free.

What did those words make you picture?_____

_____

What did you picture for...

1. the needles being removed? _____

_____

2. his skin after the needles are removed? _____

_____

3. him feeling relaxed? _____

_____

4. pain free? _____

_____

5 **Fifth Sentence:** He may return for more sessions to help with his chronic pain and to keep him in good health.

What did those words make you picture? _____

_____

What did you picture for...

1. chronic pain?_____

_____

2. him returning? _____

_____

3. how often he returns? _____

_____

Picture Summary:

Number your images in order.

[ ] The needles are poked just under the skin at certain points on the patient's body.

[ ] The needles are removed, and the patient should feel relaxed and pain free.

[ ] The needles are used for an ancient Chinese medical practice called acupuncture.

[ ] The patient may return for more acupuncture to help with his chronic pain.

14

Critical Thinking

Write a Word Summary:

_____

_____

_____

_____

Main Idea:

Check the box that best describes all your images—
the main idea.

☐ The needles used in acupuncture are long and thin and are poked in just under the skin.

☐ Acupuncture is an ancient method of using sharp thin needles that are inserted under the skin to relieve pain.

☐ A patient who is suffering from chronic pain can try an ancient Chinese medical practice.

HOT Questions:

1. Do you think it takes a trained professional to perform acupuncture? Why or why not? _____

_____

2. Why do you think it is important for the patient to lie still during acupuncture? _____

_____

3. Why do you think the needles are thin? _____

_____

4. Do you think it hurts to get acupuncture? Why or why not? _____

_____

5. Why do you think a patient may return for more sessions of acupuncture? _____

_____

6. Why do you think the patient returns for more sessions instead of having the needles left in his body? _____

_____

Make up an exciting story about someone who receives acupuncture.

_____

_____

_____

_____

_____

_____

_____

_____

_____

_____

_____

_____

_____

_____

_____

_____

_____

_____

Did you use all of the Structure Words? Check each one you used.

- ☐ What
- ☐ Size
- ☐ Number
- ☐ Shape
- ☐ Color
- ☐ Movement
- ☐ Mood
- ☐ Where
- ☐ Background
- ☐ When
- ☐ Perspective
- ☐ Sound

5 Arabia

The desert of Arabia is a harsh place where there are no lakes or running streams and few plants. During the days of summer, the blazing sun heats the sand and air to over 130 degrees Fahrenheit. With no plants to trap the heat, the winter nights are so cold that if there was any water, it might freeze. Winds rage over the brown sand, lifting it into swirling siroccos that race across the open ground. The powerful winds sculpt the sand into tall sloping dunes several hundred feet high.

Vocabulary to Visualize:

Arabia: a country in the Middle East, now known as Saudi Arabia
harsh: difficult, unpleasant
Fahrenheit: a system of measuring temperature
siroccos: tornadoes of sand
dunes: large hills of sand

---

1 **First Sentence:** The desert of Arabia is a harsh place where there are no lakes or running streams and few plants.

What did those words make you picture?_____
_____

What did you picture for...

1. the desert of Arabia?_____
_____

2. a "harsh" place?_____
_____

3. a land with no lakes?_____
_____

4. few plants?_____
_____

---

2 **Second Sentence:** During the days of summer, the blazing sun heats the sand and air to over 130 degrees Fahrenheit.

What did those words make you picture?_____
_____

What did you picture for...

1. the blazing sun?_____
_____

2. the summer days?_____
_____

3. the sun heating the sand?_____
_____

4. the hot air?_____
_____

3 **Third Sentence:** With no plants to trap the heat, the winter nights are so cold that if there was any water, it might freeze.

What did those words make you picture? _____

_____

_____

What did you picture for...

1. the winter nights? _____

_____

2. how cold it is at night? _____

_____

3. the water? _____

_____

4. water freezing? _____

_____

4 **Fourth Sentence:** Winds rage over the brown sand, lifting it into swirling siroccos that race across the open ground.

What did those words make you picture? _____

_____

_____

What did you picture for...

1. the raging winds? _____

_____

2. the wind lifting the sand? _____

_____

3. a sirocco? _____

_____

4. it racing across the ground? _____

_____

5 **Fifth Sentence:** The powerful winds sculpt the sand into tall sloping dunes several hundred feet high.

What did those words make you picture? _____

_____

_____

What did you picture for...

1. the sand being sculpted? _____

_____

2. the dunes? _____

_____

3. the dunes being so high? _____

_____

Picture Summary:

Number your images in order.

☐ The winds are powerful and form the sand into high sloping dunes.

☐ The winter nights are so cold that water might freeze, if there was any in the desert.

☐ The raging winds pick up sand and swirl it into fast-moving siroccos.

☐ The desert has few plants and little water, and temperatures can get up to 130 degrees Fahrenheit on a summer day.

Critical Thinking

Write a Word Summary:

_____

_____

_____

_____

Main Idea:

Check the box that best describes all your images—the main idea.

☐ The sand of the desert in Arabia can get very hot or very cold, depending on whether it is winter or summer.

☐ The blazing hot sun heats the sand and air to an extreme temperature of 130 degrees Fahrenheit on a typical summer day.

☐ The desert in Arabia is a harsh place where the temperatures are extreme and the winds are strong.

HOT Questions:

1. Why do you think the desert in Arabia is considered a "harsh" place? _____

_____

2. Do you think many people live in the desert of Arabia? Explain. _____

_____

3. Why might there be no lakes or running streams in the desert? _____

_____

4. Why might siroccos be common in the desert of Arabia? _____

_____

5. How do you think the wind sculpts the dunes? _____

_____

6. Why do you think the dunes get so high? _____

_____

Make up an adventure about being stuck in the desert of Arabia for a day and a night.

_____

_____

_____

_____

_____

_____

_____

_____

_____

_____

_____

_____

_____

_____

_____

_____

_____

_____

_____

Did you use all of the Structure Words? Check each one you used.

☐ What   ☐ Number   ☐ Color   ☐ Mood   ☐ Background   ☐ Perspective
☐ Size   ☐ Shape   ☐ Movement   ☐ Where   ☐ When   ☐ Sound

6 Horseshoe Crab

The horseshoe crab is an ocean-dwelling animal with a hard shell shaped like the hoof of a horse. The brown curved shell covers and protects the crab's soft body and has two small holes in it for his eyes. At night, he uses his back five pairs of legs to walk on the sandy ocean bottom. Then he digs in the sand with his two pincer front legs looking for clams or worms to grab and eat. As he digs, he steadies himself with his long pointy tail that sticks out from the rear of his body.

Vocabulary to Visualize:

hoof: the hard part of a horse's foot
pincer: large claw like on a crab or lobster
clams: soft-bodied sea creatures with two hard shells covering them
steadies: firms or stabilizes

---

1 **First Sentence:** The horseshoe crab is an ocean-dwelling animal with a hard shell shaped like the hoof of a horse.

What did those words make you picture? _____

_____

_____

What did you picture for...

1. the horseshoe crab? _____

_____

2. his hard shell? _____

_____

3. the hoof of a horse? _____

_____

4. the ocean? _____

_____

2 **Second Sentence:** The brown curved shell covers and protects the crab's soft body and has two small holes in it for his eyes.

What did those words make you picture? _____

_____

_____

What did you picture for...

1. the color and shape of his shell? _____

_____

2. his soft body? _____

_____

3. the two holes? _____

_____

4. his eyes? _____

_____

3 **Third Sentence:** At night he uses his back five pairs of legs to walk on the sandy ocean bottom.

What did those words make you picture?_____

_____

_____

What did you picture for...

1. his legs? _____

_____

2. him walking? _____

_____

3. where his five pairs of legs are?_____

_____

4. the ocean bottom? _____

_____

4 **Fourth Sentence:** Then he digs in the sand with his two pincer front legs looking for clams or worms to grab and eat.

What did those words make you picture?_____

_____

_____

What did you picture for...

1. his two front legs? _____

_____

2. him digging in the sand? _____

_____

3. a clam? _____

_____

4. him grabbing a clam? _____

_____

5 **Fifth Sentence:** As he digs, he steadies himself with his long pointy tail that sticks out from the rear of his body.

What did those words make you picture? _____

_____

_____

What did you picture for...

1. his tail? _____

_____

2. where his tail sticks out from? _____

_____

3. him using his tail to steady himself? _____

_____

Picture Summary:

Number your images in order.

☐ The horseshoe crab uses his pincer front legs to dig in the sand for clams or worms to eat.

☐ The horseshoe crab has a curved hard shell to cover and protect his soft body.

☐ The horseshoe crab walks on the ocean bottom at night with his five pairs of legs.

☐ The horseshoe crab steadies himself with his long pointy tail as he digs.

Write a Word Summary:

_____

_____

_____

_____

Main Idea:

Check the box that best describes all your images—the main idea.

☐ The horseshoe crab has a hard curved shell that is shaped like a horse's hoof which protects his soft body.

☐ The horseshoe crab looks for clams and worms to eat, digging them out of the sand with his front pincers.

☐ The horseshoe crab scurries along the sandy ocean bottom, running from danger until he can dig a hole to hide in.

HOT Questions:

1. Why do you think it is important for the horseshoe crab to be covered by a hard shell?_____

_____

2. Why do you think it is important for the shell of the crab to have two holes for his eyes?_____

_____

3. Why do you think it is important that his two front legs are pincers? _____

_____

4. How do you think the crab uses his tail to steady himself as he digs?_____

_____

5. Why might the horseshoe crab eat worms instead of fish? _____

_____

6. Why do you think this creature is called a horseshoe crab?_____

_____

Make up a story about a hungry horseshoe crab searching the ocean bottom for food.

_____

_____

_____

_____

_____

_____

_____

_____

_____

_____

_____

_____

_____

_____

_____

_____

_____

Did you use all of the Structure Words? Check each one you used.

| ☐ What | ☐ Number | ☐ Color | ☐ Mood | ☐ Background | ☐ Perspective |
| ☐ Size | ☐ Shape | ☐ Movement | ☐ Where | ☐ When | ☐ Sound |

7 Hubble Space Telescope

Rocket engines thundered at the rear of the white space shuttle as it lifted off the ground. Bright orange flames ripped through the sky, pushing the ship faster than a bullet into outer space. While they floated in orbit, the astronauts put on their bulky white space suits and opened the doors of the shuttle. The three men carefully lifted the Hubble Space Telescope out of the cramped cargo bay and into space. The telescope will take vivid pictures of planets and stars and send them down to Earth.

Vocabulary to Visualize:

telescope: an instrument used to make far off things appear closer and larger
rocket: a missile used to launch things up into outer space
space shuttle: a vehicle for flying in space
orbit: a path in space followed by a planet, moon, or ship
vivid: very clear, with lots of detail

---

1 First Sentence: Rocket engines thundered at the rear of the white space shuttle as it lifted off the ground.

What did those words make you picture? _____

_____

_____

What did you picture for...

1. the space shuttle? _____

_____

2. rocket engines? _____

_____

3. the shuttle lifting off the ground? _____

_____

4. the thundering sound? _____

_____

---

2 Second Sentence: Bright orange flames ripped through the sky, pushing the ship faster than a bullet into outer space.

What did those words make you picture? _____

_____

_____

What did you picture for...

1. the orange flames? _____

_____

2. the flames pushing the ship? _____

_____

3. the ship flying into the sky? _____

_____

4. outer space? _____

_____

3 **Third Sentence:** While they floated in orbit, the astronauts put on their bulky white space suits and opened the doors of the shuttle.

What did those words make you picture? _____

_____

_____

What did you picture for...

1. the astronauts? _____

_____

2. their space suits? _____

_____

3. the doors of the shuttle? _____

_____

4. the men opening the doors? _____

_____

4 **Fourth Sentence:** The three men carefully lifted the Hubble Space Telescope out of the cramped cargo bay and into space.

What did those words make you picture? _____

_____

_____

What did you picture for...

1. the telescope? _____

_____

2. the men lifting it? _____

_____

3. the cargo bay? _____

_____

4. the telescope in space? _____

_____

5 **Fifth Sentence:** The telescope will take vivid pictures of planets and stars and send them down to Earth.

What did those words make you picture? _____

_____

_____

What did you picture for...

1. the planets? _____

_____

2. the stars? _____

_____

3. the telescope's pictures? _____

_____

Picture Summary:

Number your images in order.

◻ The space shuttle lifted into the air, powered by rocket engines.

◻ The telescope will take pictures of planets and stars and send the pictures back to Earth.

◻ The astronauts carefully lifted the telescope out of the cargo bay and into space.

◻ The astronauts put on their bulky spacesuits and opened the shuttle's doors.

26

Critical Thinking

Write a Word Summary:

_____

_____

_____

_____

_____

Main Idea:

Check the box that best describes all your images—the main idea.

☐ The three astronauts went up into space aboard a white space shuttle so they could study the stars and planets.

☐ The astronauts opened the shuttle doors carefully and then set the Hubble Space Telescope in place.

☐ The Hubble Space Telescope, set up by astronauts in space, takes pictures of stars and planets and sends them to Earth.

HOT Questions:

1. Why do you think it is important for the shuttle to have rocket engines? _____

_____

2. Why do you think the astronauts have to wear space suits? _____

_____

3. Why might people on Earth want the telescope to be set up in space? _____

_____

4. Why do you think it might be important for people on Earth to have pictures of planets and stars? _____

_____

5. What do you think the astronauts did after they finished lifting the telescope? _____

_____

6. Do you think it was difficult to get the Hubble Space Telescope into space? Why or why not? _____

_____

Make up a story about a space adventure.

_____

_____

_____

_____

_____

_____

_____

_____

_____

_____

_____

_____

_____

_____

_____

_____

Did you use all of the Structure Words? Check each one you used.

☐ What ☐ Number ☐ Color ☐ Mood ☐ Background ☐ Perspective
☐ Size ☐ Shape ☐ Movement ☐ Where ☐ When ☐ Sound

8 Tamerlane

As a poor boy in a small town in Asia, the warrior Tamerlane came up with a plan to rule the world. At thirty-four, the fierce warlord set out with his army to destroy every town and farm on their march south. The huge army of men and elephants swept through the land, burning the villages they raided. The "Earthshaker," as Tamerlane was called, then built himself the finest city in Asia and filled it with palaces. Artisans were brought there to create silks, tiles, and art for his empire, which thrived for seven years.

Vocabulary to Visualize:

Asia: a continent that includes China and Russia
warrior: a fighter or soldier
warlord: the leader of an army
artisans: people skilled in an art
silks: material made by silkworms; very soft and rare fabric

---

1 **First Sentence:** As a poor boy in a small town in Asia, the warrior Tamerlane came up with a plan to rule the world.

What did those words make you picture?_____

_____

What did you picture for...

1. the warrior Tamerlane?_____

_____

2. him as a poor boy? _____

_____

3. his small town? _____

_____

4. him planning? _____

---

2 **Second Sentence:** At thirty-four, the fierce warlord set out with his army to destroy every town and farm on their march south.

What did those words make you picture?_____

_____

What did you picture for...

1. him at thirty-four? _____

_____

2. him as a fierce warlord?_____

_____

3. his army destroying towns?_____

_____

4. them marching on?_____

3 **Third Sentence:** The huge army of men and elephants swept through the land, burning the villages they raided.

What did those words make you picture? _____

_____

_____

What did you picture for...

1. the huge army? _____

_____

2. the elephants? _____

_____

3. them sweeping through the land? _____

_____

4. them burning the villages? _____

_____

4 **Fourth Sentence:** The "Earthshaker," as Tamerlane was called, then built himself the finest city in Asia and filled it with palaces.

What did those words make you picture? _____

_____

_____

What did you picture for...

1. "Earthshaker"? _____

_____

2. the city? _____

_____

3. the palaces? _____

_____

4. how many palaces? _____

_____

5 **Fifth Sentence:** Artisans were brought there to create silks, tiles, and art for his empire, which thrived for seven years.

What did those words make you picture? _____

_____

_____

What did you picture for...

1. artisans? _____

_____

2. silks? _____

_____

3. Tamerlane's empire? _____

_____

Picture Summary:

Number your images in order.

▮ Tamerlane planned to rule the world even as a poor boy growing up in an Asian town.

▮ Tamerlane was known as the "Earthshaker."

▮ Tamerlane set out at the age of thirty-four with a huge cruel army, marching south and destroying everything in his path.

▮ Tamerlane built the finest city in Asia, bringing in artisans to make art, silks, and tiles for his empire.

Critical Thinking

Write a Word Summary:

_____

_____

_____

_____

Main Idea:

Check the box that best describes all your images—the main idea.

☐ Tamerlane set out to build the finest city in Asia, with palaces and silks, art, and tiles created by skilled artisans.

☐ Tamerlane began planning his takeover of the world as a little boy growing up in a small town in Asia.

☐ Tamerlane set out to rule the world with his army of men and elephants, and then built the finest city in Asia.

HOT Questions:

1. Why do you think Tamerlane might have wanted to rule the world? _____

_____

2. What does it say about Tamerlane that he planned to rule the world since childhood? _____

_____

3. Why do you think he needed a huge army? _____

_____

4. How might elephants have helped Tamerlane and his army? _____

_____

5. Why do you think Tamerlane was called the "Earthshaker"? _____

_____

6. Why do you think Tamerlane wanted to build the finest city in Asia? _____

_____

Make up a terrifying story about a town when Tamerlane came through.

_____

_____

_____

_____

_____

_____

_____

_____

_____

_____

_____

_____

_____

_____

_____

_____

_____

_____

_____

_____

Did you use all of the Structure Words? Check each one you used.

- ☐ What
- ☐ Size
- ☐ Number
- ☐ Shape
- ☐ Color
- ☐ Movement
- ☐ Mood
- ☐ Where
- ☐ Background
- ☐ When
- ☐ Perspective
- ☐ Sound

9

Wyatt Earp

Wyatt Earp, a tall man with a big moustache, was a U.S. marshal in the frontier town of Tombstone. Wyatt and his two brothers tried to keep the peace, using guns to police the violent wild west. His most famous gunfight was near the O.K. Corral, with his brothers, against a gang of cattle rustlers. The Earps were trying to arrest the gang when shooting suddenly broke out and left most of the thieves dead. Some townspeople said the Earps fired first while others thought the gang started the fight, but no one knows.

Vocabulary to Visualize:

Wyatt Earp: a gambler, gunfighter, and U.S. Marshal who lived from 1848-1929
marshal: a person granted the power to act as a sheriff or policeman
Tombstone: a lawless mining town in the Arizona Territory in the 1800s
gunfight: when two or more people are firing guns at each other
rustlers: cattle thieves

---

1 **First Sentence:** Wyatt Earp, a tall man with a big moustache, was a U.S. marshal in the frontier town of Tombstone.

What did those words make you picture?_____
_____
_____

What did you picture for...

1. Wyatt Earp? _____
   _____

2. his moustache? _____
   _____

3. a U.S. marshal? _____
   _____

4. Tombstone? _____
   _____

---

2 **Second Sentence:** Wyatt and his two brothers tried to keep the peace, using guns to police the violent wild west.

What did those words make you picture?_____
_____
_____

What did you picture for...

1. Wyatt's brothers? _____
   _____

2. Wyatt keeping peace? _____
   _____

3. their guns? _____
   _____

4. the wild west? _____
   _____

3 **Third Sentence:** His most famous gunfight was near the O.K. Corral, with his brothers, against a gang of cattle rustlers.

What did those words make you picture? _____

_____

_____

What did you picture for...

1. the O.K. Corral? _____

_____

2. Wyatt and his brothers near the corral? _____

_____

3. the cattle rustlers? _____

_____

4. a gunfight? _____

_____

4 **Fourth Sentence:** The Earps were trying to arrest the gang when shooting suddenly broke out and left most of the thieves dead.

What did those words make you picture? _____

_____

_____

What did you picture for...

1. the attempted arrest? _____

_____

2. the sounds of the shooting? _____

_____

3. most of the thieves dead? _____

_____

4. the time of day? _____

_____

5 **Fifth Sentence:** Some townspeople said the Earps fired first while others thought the gang started the fight, but no one knows.

What did those words make you picture? _____

_____

_____

What did you picture for...

1. the townspeople talking? _____

_____

2. the Earps firing first? _____

_____

3. the sounds in this imagery? _____

Picture Summary:

Number your images in order.

☐ Wyatt Earp was a marshal in the wild west town of Tombstone, where his brothers were also lawmen.

☐ The Earps and some cattle rustlers faced off near the O.K. Corral.

☐ The people of the town were split between thinking that the Earps fired first or that the gang of thieves fired first.

☐ Earp and his brothers tried to arrest the thieves when shooting broke out.

Write a Word Summary:

_____

_____

_____

_____

_____

Main Idea:

Check the box that best describes all your images—the main idea.

☐ Tombstone was a wild west frontier town where Wyatt Earp and his two brothers were deputy U.S. marshals.

☐ The Earp brothers were cattle rustlers who faced off with marshals near the O.K. Corral in a famous gun battle.

☐ Marshal Wyatt Earp and his brothers tried to arrest a gang of cattle rustlers, but instead a gunfight broke out at the O.K. Corral.

HOT Questions:

1. Why do you think Wyatt Earp had to use his gun to keep peace? _____

_____

2. Why do you think it was important for Wyatt to keep the peace in Tombstone? _____

_____

3. Why might Wyatt have had his brothers help him with the arrest at the O.K. Corral? _____

_____

4. Why do you think he and his brothers tried to arrest the gang? _____

_____

5. Why do you think the gunfight may have broken out? _____

_____

6. Do you think that the Earp brothers fired first or that the cattle rustlers fired first? Why? _____

_____

Make up an exciting story about the gunfight at the O.K. Corral.

_____

_____

_____

_____

_____

_____

_____

_____

_____

_____

_____

_____

_____

_____

Did you use all of the Structure Words? Check each one you used.

☐ What	☐ Number	☐ Color	☐ Mood	☐ Background	☐ Perspective
☐ Size	☐ Shape	☐ Movement	☐ Where	☐ When	☐ Sound

10 Landing on Mars

The outside of the unmanned spaceship glowed red hot as it streaked across the Martian sky, leaving a smoky trail. The thick heat shield on the outside of the ship kept it from burning up as the ship entered the atmosphere. When it slowed, a white parachute opened and the ship floated silently down toward the red rocky ground of Mars. Close to the ground, balloons inflated all around it, the parachute came off, and the ship bounced to a stop. Then the ship's big doors opened up so the six-wheeled robot rover could roll out and explore the strange planet.

Vocabulary to Visualize:

Mars: a planet in our solar system
unmanned: with no people on board
Martian: of or from Mars
atmosphere: the mix of gases surrounding a planet; the air
parachute: a large sheet that unfolds like an umbrella and causes something to fall slowly
inflate: fill with air or gas
rover: a type of vehicle

---

1 **First Sentence:** The outside of the unmanned spaceship glowed red hot as it streaked across the Martian sky, leaving a smoky trail.

What did those words make you picture? _____

_____

_____

What did you picture for...

1. the spaceship? _____

_____

2. it streaking across the sky? _____

_____

3. a smoky trail? _____

_____

4. the Martian sky? _____

_____

---

2 **Second Sentence:** The thick heat shield on the outside of the ship kept it from burning up as the ship entered the atmosphere.

What did those words make you picture? _____

_____

_____

What did you picture for...

1. the heat shield? _____

_____

2. the outside of the ship? _____

_____

3. how hot the shield gets? _____

_____

4. the atmosphere? _____

_____

3 **Third Sentence:** When it slowed, a white parachute opened and the ship floated silently down toward the red rocky ground of Mars.

What did those words make you picture? _____

_____

_____

What did you picture for...

1. the parachute? _____

_____

2. the parachute opening? _____

_____

3. the ship floating? _____

_____

4. the rocky ground of Mars? _____

_____

4 **Fourth Sentence:** Close to the ground, balloons inflated all around it, the parachute came off, and the ship bounced to a stop.

What did those words make you picture? _____

_____

_____

What did you picture for...

1. the ship close to the ground? _____

_____

2. the inflated balloons? _____

_____

3. where the balloons were? _____

_____

4. the ship bouncing? _____

_____

5 **Fifth Sentence:** Then the ship's big doors opened up so the six-wheeled robot rover could roll out and explore the strange planet.

What did those words make you picture? _____

_____

_____

What did you picture for...

1. the ship's doors opening? _____

_____

2. the robot rover? _____

_____

3. the rover exploring? _____

_____

Picture Summary:

Number your images in order.

☐ The ship bounced to a stop, then opened up so the robot rover could roll out to explore the planet.

☐ The outside of the unmanned ship glowed red as it flew across Mars' sky, protected by a heat shield.

☐ A white parachute opened and the ship silently floated toward the red ground of Mars.

☐ The parachute fell off and balloons inflated all around the ship.

Critical Thinking

Write a Word Summary:

_____

_____

_____

_____

Main Idea:

Check the box that best describes all your images—the main idea.

- [ ] The unmanned spaceship landed on Mars using a parachute and a robot rover rolled out of it to explore the planet.

- [ ] There were balloons all over the ship that inflated to allow the ship to bounce to a stop on the red rocky ground of Mars.

- [ ] The unmanned spaceship glowed red with heat as it streaked through the Earth's sky, protected by a thick heat shield.

HOT Questions:

1. Why do you think the spaceship glowed red-hot? _____

_____

2. Why might the spaceship have needed a heat shield? _____

_____

3. Why do you think it needed a parachute? _____

_____

4. Why do you think balloons might have been important for the ship? _____

_____

5. Why do you think the robot rover was needed? _____

_____

6. Who do you think controlled the rover? _____

_____

Make up a story about what the rover might see or find on Mars.

_____

_____

_____

_____

_____

_____

_____

_____

_____

_____

_____

_____

_____

_____

_____

Did you use all of the Structure Words? Check each one you used.

- ☐ What
- ☐ Size
- ☐ Number
- ☐ Shape
- ☐ Color
- ☐ Movement
- ☐ Mood
- ☐ Where
- ☐ Background
- ☐ When
- ☐ Perspective
- ☐ Sound

11 Florence Nightingale

Florence Nightingale was shocked by the dirty hospital where she was a nurse during the Crimean War. Injured soldiers lay on the floors and rats scampered over them. / The nurses knew little and there was no soap or towels to wash with. Florence cleaned up and wrote many letters to get supplies from home. / Just under the dusty wood floor, smelly sewers flowed past. Florence had the floors scrubbed clean and she made sure that each patient had a fresh bed. / She taught her fellow nurses that a clean ward could stop infection. Florence's efforts helped hospitals to become cleaner and she became famous as a nurse.

Vocabulary to Visualize:

Florence Nightingale: a nurse who lived from 1820-1910 and changed nursing for the better during the Crimean War

Crimean War: a war between Britain, France, and Russia in 1854

scampered: ran very fast

ward: a section of a hospital

infection: disease or sickness caused by germs or bacteria that may lead to death

---

1 **First and Second Sentences:** Florence Nightingale was shocked by the dirty hospital where she was a nurse during the Crimean War. Injured soldiers lay on the floors and rats scampered over them.

What did those words make you picture? _____

_____

What did you picture for...

1. Florence Nightingale as a nurse? _____

_____

2. the hospital? _____

_____

3. injured soldiers? _____

_____

4. rats? _____

_____

---

2 **Third and Fourth Sentences:** The nurses knew little and there was no soap or towels to wash with. Florence cleaned up and wrote many letters to get supplies from home.

What did those words make you picture? _____

_____

What did you picture for...

1. the nurses? _____

_____

2. Florence cleaning? _____

_____

3. her writing letters? _____

_____

4. the supplies? _____

_____

3 **Fifth and Sixth Sentences:** Just under the dusty wood floor, smelly sewers flowed past. Florence had the floors scrubbed clean and she made sure that each patient had a fresh bed.

What did those words make you picture?_____

_____

_____

What did you picture for...

1. the floor? _____

_____

2. the smell of the sewers? _____

_____

3. the floors being scrubbed? _____

_____

4. the fresh beds? _____

4 **Seventh and Eighth Sentences:** She taught her fellow nurses that a clean ward could stop infection. Florence's efforts helped hospitals to become cleaner and she became famous as a nurse.

What did those words make you picture?_____

_____

_____

What did you picture for...

1. Florence teaching? _____

_____

2. the other nurses? _____

_____

3. infection? _____

_____

4. a clean ward? _____

_____

Picture Summary:

Number your images in order.

[ ] Florence taught the other nurses to be cleaner to stop infection.

[ ] Florence was shocked by the hospital's dirty conditions during the Crimean War.

[ ] Florence got the wounded off the floor, cleaned the ward and set up clean beds.

[ ] Florence worked in an army hospital where rats were everywhere.

Write a Word Summary:

_____

_____

_____

_____

_____

_____

_____

Critical Thinking

Main Idea:

Check the box that best describes all your images—the main idea.

☐ Florence Nightingale saved many lives by working as a nurse during the war in a city hospital.

☐ Florence Nightingale was disgusted by the conditions in the army hospital, which included rats, sewers, and dirt all over the floor.

☐ Florence Nightingale worked as a nurse and improved the cleanliness of an army hospital and taught nurses to better save lives.

HOT Questions:

1. Why do you think Florence Nightingale was shocked by the army hospital? _____

_____

2. Why do you think rats scampered all around the wounded men? _____

_____

3. Why do you think Florence wanted cleaner conditions? _____

_____

4. Why do you think Florence wrote letters home? _____

_____

5. Why do you think it was important to get the wounded off the floor? _____

_____

6. Why do you think it was important that Florence teach the other nurses? _____

_____

7. Why do you think she is famous as a nurse? _____

_____

Make up a story about being Florence Nightingale in a dirty hospital.

_____

_____

_____

_____

_____

_____

_____

_____

_____

_____

_____

_____

_____

_____

Did you use all of the Structure Words? Check each one you used.

- ☐ What
- ☐ Size
- ☐ Number
- ☐ Shape
- ☐ Color
- ☐ Movement
- ☐ Mood
- ☐ Where
- ☐ Background
- ☐ When
- ☐ Perspective
- ☐ Sound

12 Fireworks

Fireworks explode into sparks of bright colors and loud noises high in the night sky. Each one begins as a hollow paper tube packed with coarse and fine gunpowder. / A fuse is lit, which reaches the coarse packed gunpowder. This shoots the tube rocket up in the air at a very high speed. / The fine gunpowder explodes next. It makes a huge blast of bright light along with a loud boom. / Chemicals in the powder cause the light to change color. Bits of burning metal add sparkling showers.

Vocabulary to Visualize:

fireworks: colorful explosives used for celebrations or shows
coarse: rough, thick
gunpowder: an explosive mixture of powder
coarse: rough, thick
fuse: a string or wick attached to an explosive that is lit to set it off
chemicals: small natural particles or material

---

1 **First and Second Sentences:** Fireworks explode into sparks of bright colors and loud noises high in the night sky. Each one begins as a hollow paper tube packed with coarse and fine gunpowder.

What did those words make you picture? _____

_____

What did you picture for...

1. fireworks? _____

_____

2. a paper tube? _____

_____

3. the coarse gunpowder? _____

_____

4. the gunpowder in the tube? _____

---

2 **Third and Fourth Sentences:** A fuse is lit, which reaches the coarse packed gunpowder. This shoots the tube rocket up in the air at a very high speed.

What did those words make you picture? _____

_____

What did you picture for...

1. a fuse? _____

_____

2. the fuse being lit? _____

_____

3. the tube shooting up in the air? _____

_____

4. how fast it shoots up? _____

3 **Fifth and Sixth Sentences:** The fine gunpowder explodes next. It makes a huge blast of bright light along with a loud boom.

What did those words make you picture?_____

_____

_____

What did you picture for...

1. the fine gunpowder?_____

_____

2. the powder exploding?_____

_____

3. the sound it makes?_____

_____

4. when this is happening?_____

_____

4 **Seventh and Eighth Sentences:** Chemicals in the powder cause the light to change color. Bits of burning metal add sparkling showers.

What did those words make you picture?_____

_____

_____

What did you picture for...

1. the light changing color?_____

_____

2. bits of metal?_____

_____

3. the metal burning?_____

_____

4. sparkling showers?_____

_____

Picture Summary:

Number your images in order.

☐ Fireworks start out as a hollow paper tube stuffed with coarse and fine gunpowder.

☐ The coarse gunpowder in a firework explodes first, shooting the tube high into the sky.

☐ Bits of metal and chemicals mixed in the gunpowder burn and create effects.

☐ The fine gunpowder explodes high in the air, causing the blast of light and the booming sound.

Write a Word Summary:

_____

_____

_____

_____

_____

_____

_____

Critical Thinking

Main Idea:

Check the box that best describes all your images—the main idea.

☐ Fireworks are explosions of bright color and loud booms that start out as tubes packed with gunpowder, chemicals, and metal.

☐ Coarse and fine gunpowder are packed tightly into small paper tubes that are lit by a fuse that hangs off of the tube.

☐ Fireworks can be many colors, depending on the types of chemicals that are put in the paper tube along with gunpowder.

HOT Questions:

1. Why do you think gunpowder is put in fireworks? _____

_____

2. Why do you think both coarse and fine gunpowder are used? _____

_____

3. Why do you think chemicals are put in fireworks? _____

_____

4. Why do you think the fuse of a firework has to be lit? _____

_____

5. Why do you think fireworks are shot up into the sky? _____

_____

6. Do you think it would be better to shoot fireworks during the day or at night? Explain. _____

_____

7. What do you think fireworks are used for? _____

_____

Make up a story about something funny happening during an incredible fireworks show.

_____

_____

_____

_____

_____

_____

_____

_____

_____

_____

_____

_____

_____

_____

_____

Did you use all of the Structure Words? Check each one you used.

☐ What	☐ Number	☐ Color	☐ Mood	☐ Background	☐ Perspective
☐ Size	☐ Shape	☐ Movement	☐ Where	☐ When	☐ Sound

13 A Wedding in India

A wedding in India is a joyful celebration that lasts at least five days. It begins with a prayer ceremony for the bride and groom. / This is followed by days of feasts with family and friends. The day before the wedding, designs are painted on the bride's arms and legs with brown henna dye. / On her wedding day, the bride dresses in a red sari trimmed with gold and jewels. More jewels adorn her black hair and gold bracelets cover her wrists and arms. / She weds her groom under a canopy of flowers in front of hundreds of guests. Then there is a huge banquet with food, music, and dancing.

Vocabulary to Visualize:

India: a country in South Asia
celebration: a party or festival
ceremony: a formal event with rituals
henna: a dye used for temporary tattoos
sari: a long piece of cotton or silk worn as a wrap around the body
adorn: decorate
canopy: a covering; shelter
banquet: a large dinner party

---

1 **First and Second Sentences:** A wedding in India is a joyful celebration that lasts at least five days. It begins with a prayer ceremony for the bride and groom.

What did those words make you picture?_____

_____

What did you picture for...

1. a wedding in India? _____

_____

2. a joyful celebration? _____

_____

3. the bride and groom? _____

_____

4. the prayer ceremony? _____

_____

---

2 **Third and Fourth Sentences:** This is followed by days of feasts with family and friends. The day before the wedding, designs are painted on the bride's arms and legs with brown henna dye.

What did those words make you picture?_____

_____

What did you picture for...

1. feasts? _____

_____

2. the henna dye? _____

_____

3. the designs being painted on? _____

_____

4. the designs on the bride's arms and legs? _____

_____

3 **Fifth and Sixth Sentences:** On her wedding day, the bride dresses in a red sari trimmed with gold and jewels. More jewels adorn her black hair and gold bracelets cover her wrists and arms.

What did those words make you picture?_____

_____

_____

What did you picture for...

1. the bride on her wedding day? _____

_____

2. her red sari? _____

_____

3. the gold and jewels on the sari? _____

_____

4. her hair? _____

_____

4 **Seventh and Eighth Sentences:** She weds her groom under a canopy of flowers in front of hundreds of guests. Then there is a huge banquet with food, music, and dancing.

What did those words make you picture?_____

_____

_____

What did you picture for...

1. the bride and groom being wed?_____

_____

2. the canopy of flowers? _____

_____

3. the guests? _____

_____

4. the banquet? _____

_____

Picture Summary:

Number your images in order.

☐ The bride and groom wed under a canopy of flowers while their friends and family watch.

☐ The day before the wedding, the bride gets henna designs painted on her legs and arms.

☐ The bride dresses in a red sari that is lined with gold and jewels.

☐ A huge banquet follows the wedding ceremony.

Write a Word Summary:

_____

_____

_____

_____

_____

_____

_____

Critical Thinking

Main Idea:

Check the box that best describes all your images—the main idea.

☐ An Indian wedding is a time of celebration and ceremony with rituals, family and friends, and feasts.

☐ The bride in an Indian wedding first has henna designs painted on her legs and arms and then dresses in a red sari that is adorned with gold and jewels.

☐ The bride and groom of an Indian wedding have a joyful time painting henna designs on their arms and legs.

HOT Questions:

1. Why do you think a wedding in India is a joyous time? _____

_____

2. Why do you think the celebration lasts for five days? _____

_____

3. Why do you think family and friends are invited to the huge feasts? _____

_____

4. Why do you think the bride dresses up on her wedding day?_____

_____

5. Why do you think there is food, music, and dancing after the bride and groom wed? _____

_____

6. Why do you think so many people attend the wedding? _____

_____

7. How is an Indian wedding different than weddings you have heard of?_____

_____

Make up a story about something funny happening during painting of the designs on the bride at an Indian wedding.

_____

_____

_____

_____

_____

_____

_____

_____

_____

_____

_____

_____

_____

_____

_____

_____

_____

_____

Did you use all of the Structure Words? Check each one you used.

☐ What	☐ Number	☐ Color	☐ Mood	☐ Background	☐ Perspective
☐ Size	☐ Shape	☐ Movement	☐ Where	☐ When	☐ Sound

14 Aesop's Fables

Aesop was an ancient Greek who wrote fables with talking animals as the characters. One of Aesop's best-known fables is "The Tortoise and the Hare." / It is about a race between the slow tortoise and the speedy hare. The hare is so sure that he will win that he takes a nap in the middle of the race. / The slow tortoise does not stop and passes right by the sleeping hare. He finally gets to the finish line, where the other animals are cheering. / He wins the race just as the hare is waking up. The moral of the story is that "slow and steady won the race."

Vocabulary to Visualize:

Aesop: a Greek writer who lived around 600 B.C.
fables: stories that teach a moral or lesson
Greek: of or from Greece
characters: the main subjects
hare: like a rabbit, but larger
tortoise: a turtle that only lives on land
moral: the lesson of the story, usually one of good conduct

---

1 **First and Second Sentences:** Aesop was an ancient Greek who wrote fables with talking animals as the characters. One of Aesop's best-known fables is "The Tortoise and the Hare."

What did those words make you picture?_____

_____

_____

What did you picture for...

1. Aesop? _____

_____

2. him writing fables? _____

_____

3. the tortoise? _____

_____

4. the hare? _____

_____

2 **Third and Fourth Sentences:** It is about a race between the slow tortoise and the speedy hare. The hare is so sure that he will win that he takes a nap in the middle of the race.

What did those words make you picture?_____

_____

_____

What did you picture for...

1. the tortoise as slow? _____

_____

2. the hare as speedy?_____

_____

3. the hare napping? _____

_____

4. where the hare naps?_____

_____

3   **Fifth and Sixth Sentences:** The slow tortoise does not stop and passes right by the sleeping hare. He finally gets to the finish line, where the other animals are cheering.

What did those words make you picture?_____

_____

_____

What did you picture for...

1.   the tortoise passing the hare? _____

_____

2.   the finish line? _____

_____

3.   the tortoise at the finish line? _____

_____

4.   the animals cheering? _____

_____

4   **Seventh and Eighth Sentences:** He wins the race just as the hare is waking up. The moral of the story is that "slow and steady won the race."

What did those words make you picture?_____

_____

_____

What did you picture for...

1.   the tortoise winning the race?_____

_____

2.   the hare waking up?_____

_____

3.   the hare's mood? _____

_____

4.   "slow and steady"?_____

_____

Picture Summary:

Number your images in order.

    The tortoise crosses the finish line just as the hare is waking up.

    The hare and the tortoise race to see who is fast.

    The hare is so sure he will win that he takes a nap, and the tortoise passes right by him.

    One of Aesop's best-known fables is about a tortoise and a hare.

Write a Word Summary:

_____

_____

_____

_____

_____

_____

Critical Thinking

Main Idea:

Check the box that best describes all your images—the main idea.

☐ Aesop, an ancient Greek, wrote stories about animals that ran races, like the tortoise and the hare.

☐ Aesop's fable, about the tortoise and the hare, teaches that "slow and steady won the race."

☐ The hare is so sure he will win the race that he stops to have a nap at the side of the road.

HOT Questions:

1. Why do you think Aesop used animal characters in his stories? _____

_____

2. Why do you think he made the animals talk like humans? _____

_____

3. Why do you think the hare was so sure that he would win the race? _____

_____

4. Why do you think he decided to take a nap? _____

_____

5. Why do you think the tortoise did not stop to rest? _____

_____

6. What do you think the moral of the story "slow and steady won the race" means? _____

_____

7. Why do you think Aesop taught morals through his stories? _____

_____

Make up an exciting story about the tortoise and the hare racing.

_____

_____

_____

_____

_____

_____

_____

_____

_____

_____

_____

_____

_____

Did you use all of the Structure Words? Check each one you used.

☐ What	☐ Number	☐ Color	☐ Mood	☐ Background	☐ Perspective
☐ Size	☐ Shape	☐ Movement	☐ Where	☐ When	☐ Sound

15 The Seahorse

The seahorse is a little fish that has a head shaped like that of a horse. He has a long snout with a tiny mouth at the end that he uses to suck up his food. / In an upright position, he waves his back fin to slowly swim through seaweed in the sea. When he spots a piece of sea grass, he curls his long tail around it. / Then he changes his color to blend with his setting so predators cannot see him. Inside a pouch on his belly, he is carrying hundreds of eggs. / He will carry the eggs in his pouch until they are ready to hatch into little seahorses.

Vocabulary to Visualize:

seahorse: a fish with a long tail and a head that resembles a horse
snout: nose
waves: moves gently back and forth
seaweed: plants that grow in the ocean
curls: wraps around
blend: to mix smoothly with
predators: animals that hunt and eat other animals

---

1 **First and Second Sentences:** The seahorse is a little fish that has a head shaped like that of a horse. He has a long snout with a tiny mouth at the end that he uses to suck up his food.

What did those words make you picture?_____

_____

What did you picture for...

1. the seahorse? _____

_____

2. the seahorse's head? _____

_____

3. the seahorse's snout? _____

_____

4. his mouth? _____

_____

---

2 **Third and Fourth Sentences:** In an upright position, he waves his back fin to slowly swim through seaweed in the sea. When he spots a piece of sea grass, he curls his long tail around it.

What did those words make you picture?_____

_____

What did you picture for...

1. the seahorse swimming? _____

_____

2. his back fin waving? _____

_____

3. the sea grass? _____

_____

4. the seahorse curling his tail around it?_____

_____

3 **Fifth and Sixth Sentences:** Then he changes his color to blend with his setting so predators cannot see him. Inside a pouch on his belly, he is carrying hundreds of eggs.

What did those words make you picture?_____

_____

_____

What did you picture for...

1. the seahorse changing color? _____

_____

2. his setting? _____

_____

3. his belly? _____

_____

4. a predator? _____

_____

4 **Seventh Sentence:** He will carry the eggs in his pouch until they are ready to hatch into little seahorses.

What did those words make you picture?_____

_____

_____

What did you picture for...

1. the eggs? _____

_____

2. the eggs inside the pouch? _____

_____

3. the eggs ready to hatch? _____

_____

4. the little seahorses? _____

_____

Picture Summary:

Number your images in order.

☐ The seahorse carries hundreds of eggs in his pouch until they are ready to hatch.

☐ The seahorse is a little fish with a head shaped like a horse.

☐ The seahorse uses his tiny mouth on the end of his long snout to suck up his food.

☐ The seahorse waves his back fin to swim and wraps his tail around a piece of sea grass to hang on.

Write a Word Summary:

_____

_____

_____

_____

_____

_____

_____

Main Idea:

Check the box that best describes all your images—the main idea.

☐ The seahorse is a small fish that swims near the surface of the water of the sea.

☐ The seahorse carries hundreds of eggs in his pouch on his belly until they are ready to hatch into little seahorses.

☐ The seahorse is a little fish that carries eggs in his pouch and hides against sea grass to avoid predators.

HOT Questions:

1. Why do you think this fish is called a seahorse? _____

_____

2. How do you think being a slow swimmer might be a problem for the seahorse? _____

_____

3. Why do you think it might be important for the seahorse to blend with his setting? _____

_____

4. Why do you think the seahorse lives among the seaweed? _____

_____

5. Why do you think it might be important for his tail to be able to curl? _____

_____

6. Why do you think it might be important for the seahorse to cling to sea grass? _____

_____

7. Why do you think it might be important for the seahorse to have a pouch on his belly? _____

_____

Make up an exciting story about a seahorse surviving an attack by a predator.

_____

_____

_____

_____

_____

_____

_____

_____

_____

_____

_____

_____

_____

_____

_____

_____

_____

Did you use all of the Structure Words? Check each one you used.

| ☐ What | ☐ Number | ☐ Color | ☐ Mood | ☐ Background | ☐ Perspective |
| ☐ Size | ☐ Shape | ☐ Movement | ☐ Where | ☐ When | ☐ Sound |

16 The First Donut

Captain Gregory invented the donut with a hole in the center. Legend says that he went to sea and took with him plenty of his mother's little cakes and her recipe. / The cakes were a Dutch treat made from leftover bread dough fried in pork fat. The captain had trouble steering his ship while holding and eating the oily cake. / So he poked the cake onto a spoke of the helm to hold it. The captain told the cook on the ship to make more cakes, but with a hole in the middle. / The new donut soon became a popular and easy to eat treat around the world.

Vocabulary to Visualize:

donut: a small cake of fried dough, usually with a hole in the middle
invented: produced or created
Dutch: of or from the Netherlands, a country in northern Europe
dough: a mixture of flour and other things like milk or water
helm: the steering wheel of a ship

---

1 **First and Second Sentences:** Captain Gregory invented the donut with a hole in the center. Legend says that he went to sea and took with him plenty of his mother's little cakes and her recipe.

What did those words make you picture? _____

_____

What did you picture for...

1. Captain Gregory? _____

_____

2. a donut? _____

_____

3. the captain at sea? _____

_____

4. his mother's cakes? _____

---

2 **Third and Fourth Sentences:** The cakes were a Dutch treat made from leftover bread dough fried in pork fat. The captain had trouble steering his ship while holding and eating the oily cake.

What did those words make you picture? _____

_____

What did you picture for...

1. bread dough? _____

_____

2. the dough being fried? _____

_____

3. the captain steering his ship? _____

_____

4. him holding the oily cake? _____

3

Fifth and Sixth Sentences: So he poked the cake onto a spoke of the helm to hold it. The captain told the cook on the ship to make more cakes, but with a hole in the middle.

What did those words make you picture? _____

_____

What did you picture for...

1. the helm? _____

_____

2. a spoke of the helm? _____

_____

3. him poking the cake onto a spoke? _____

_____

4. the captain talking to the cook? _____

_____

4

Seventh Sentence: The new donut soon became a popular and easy to eat treat around the world.

What did those words make you picture? _____

_____

What did you picture for...

1. the new donut? _____

_____

2. it being popular? _____

_____

3. it being easy to eat? _____

_____

4. around the world? _____

_____

Picture Summary:

Number your images in order.

☐ The captain poked the cake onto a spoke of the helm to free his hands.

☐ The captain told the cook on the ship to make more cakes, but with a hole in the middle.

☐ The captain went to sea and took with him some of his mother's little cakes and her recipe.

☐ The captain found it hard to steer the ship and hold the oily cake.

Write a Word Summary:

_____

_____

_____

_____

_____

_____

Main Idea:

Check the box that best describes all your images—the main idea.

☐ Captain Gregory went to sea with his mother's recipe for little cakes because he wanted to try to steer while eating one.

☐ Captain Gregory told the cook to make the little cakes like his mother's, out of bread dough fried in pork fat.

☐ Captain Gregory invented the donut with a hole in the middle while at sea.

HOT Questions:

1. Why do you think the captain took some of his mother's cakes with him on his voyage? _____

_____

2. Why do you think he wanted something to hold his oily cake while he steered? _____

_____

3. Why do you think he told the cook of the ship to make the oily cakes without centers? _____

_____

4. Why do you think it was important that he took his mother's recipe with him on the voyage? _____

_____

5. Do you think Captain Gregory's invention was a clever idea? Why or why not? _____

_____

6. How do you think having a hole in the middle improved the cake? _____

_____

7. Why do you think the captain's new donut became popular all around the world? _____

_____

Make up a story about anything you want!

_____

_____

_____

_____

_____

_____

_____

_____

_____

_____

_____

_____

_____

_____

_____

_____

Did you use all of the Structure Words? Check each one you used.

☐ What	☐ Number	☐ Color	☐ Mood	☐ Background	☐ Perspective
☐ Size	☐ Shape	☐ Movement	☐ Where	☐ When	☐ Sound

17

W.C. Fields

Before W.C. Fields became a movie star, he was a talented juggler. When he was fifteen years old, he got a performing job at an amusement park. / He wore old clothes and a fake beard to look like a hobo. He did not speak during his act, but instead used funny faces and his juggling skills to entertain the crowds. / He would fall on purpose and pretend to mess up to make them laugh. For one of his tricks, he balanced a top hat, cigar, and broom on his foot. / Then he kicked them high up into the air. He would catch the top hat on his head, the cigar in his mouth, and the broom in the pocket of his pants.

Vocabulary to Visualize:

juggler: someone who can keep two or more objects in the air at a time
amusement park: a place with rides and entertainment
hobo: someone who has no home and wanders randomly
skills: abilities

---

1 **First and Second Sentences:** Before W.C. Fields became a movie star, he was a talented juggler. When he was fifteen years old, he got a performing job at an amusement park.
What did those words make you picture? _____

_____

_____

What did you picture for...

1. W.C. Fields? _____

_____

2. a juggler? _____

_____

3. W.C. Fields at fifteen? _____

_____

4. an amusement park? _____

_____

---

2 **Third and Fourth Sentences:** He wore old clothes and a fake beard to look like a hobo. He did not speak during his act, but instead used funny faces and his juggling skills to entertain the crowds.
What did those words make you picture? _____

_____

_____

What did you picture for...

1. his clothes? _____

_____

2. his fake beard? _____

_____

3. his funny faces? _____

_____

4. the crowds? _____

_____

3 **Fifth and Sixth Sentences:** He would fall on purpose and pretend to mess up to make them laugh. For one of his tricks, he balanced a top hat, cigar, and broom on his foot.

What did those words make you picture? _____

_____

What did you picture for...

1. him falling on purpose? _____

2. him pretending to mess up? _____

3. a top hat, cigar, and broom? _____

4. them balanced on his foot? _____

4 **Seventh and Eighth Sentences:** Then he kicked them high up into the air. He would catch the top hat on his head, the cigar in his mouth, and the broom in the pocket of his pants.

What did those words make you picture? _____

_____

What did you picture for...

1. him kicking them into the air? _____

2. him catching the top hat? _____

3. him catching the cigar? _____

4. him catching the broom? _____

Picture Summary:

Number your images in order.

[ ] W.C. Fields was a talented juggler before he became a movie star.

[ ] One of W.C. Fields' tricks was to balance a cigar, top hat, and broom on his foot, kick them, and then catch them.

[ ] He dressed as a hobo, made funny faces, and did not talk as he juggled for the crowds.

[ ] W.C. Fields got a performing job at an amusement park when he was fifteen.

Write a Word Summary:

_____

_____

_____

_____

_____

Critical Thinking

Main Idea:

Check the box that best describes all your images—the main idea.

☐ W.C. Fields began his career in juggling at fifteen years old, and went on to become a movie star.

☐ W.C. Fields had a special trick where he would balance a cigar, top hat, and a broom on his foot.

☐ W.C. Fields was a famous movie star who juggled in all of his movies.

HOT Questions:

1. Why do you think W.C. Fields wore old clothes? _____

_____

2. Why do you think Fields did not speak during his act? _____

_____

3. Why do you think an amusement park was a good place for Fields to work? _____

_____

4. Why do you think it was important for him to use funny faces? _____

_____

5. Why do you think Fields was considered a funny juggler? _____

_____

6. How do you think he learned how to do the trick with the top hat, cigar, and broom? _____

_____

7. Do you think Fields liked to entertain people? Why or why not? _____

_____

Make up a story about being at an amusement park and seeing a juggler perform his act.

_____
_____
_____
_____
_____
_____
_____
_____
_____
_____
_____
_____
_____
_____
_____
_____
_____
_____
_____

Did you use all of the Structure Words? Check each one you used.

| ☐ What | ☐ Number | ☐ Color | ☐ Mood | ☐ Background | ☐ Perspective |
| ☐ Size | ☐ Shape | ☐ Movement | ☐ Where | ☐ When | ☐ Sound |

18 The Sword Smith

The sword smith ducks into his dark smithy to work on a sword. The air is thick with heat from the blistering hot fire burning in the large forge. / He puts a chunk of iron ore into the hot forge until the metal is softened and ready to shape. When he pulls the iron out with his long tongs, it is glowing bright orange. / He hammers it on his metal anvil, creating a shower of sparks with each blow. When it cools, he puts it back into the fire for a while, takes a drink of water, and rests. / Then he pulls the hot iron out again. With sweat pouring down his face, he hammers the metal flat. He repeats this for days until he has a fine hard blade for his sword.

Vocabulary to Visualize:

sword smith: someone who makes swords
smithy: the shop of a blacksmith or sword smith, used for shaping metals
sword: a sharp-edged weapon for fighting
forge: an oven for melting and heating metal
iron ore: metal in its original form
tongs: a pincer-like tool used to hold and lift
anvil: an iron or steel platform on which metal is hammered and shaped

---

1 **First and Second Sentences:** The sword smith ducks into his dark smithy to work on a sword. The air is thick with heat from the blistering hot fire burning in the large forge.

What did those words make you picture?_____

_____

What did you picture for...

1. the sword smith?_____

_____

2. the smithy?_____

_____

3. the hot fire? _____

_____

4. the forge? _____

---

2 **Third and Fourth Sentences:** He puts a chunk of iron ore into the hot forge until the metal is softened and ready to shape. When he pulls the iron out with his long tongs, it is glowing bright orange.

What did those words make you picture?_____

_____

What did you picture for...

1. the chunk of iron? _____

_____

2. him putting the iron in the forge? _____

_____

3. him pulling it out?_____

_____

4. the hot iron? _____

3 **Fifth and Sixth Sentences:** He hammers it on his metal anvil, creating a shower of sparks with each blow. When it cools, he puts it back into the fire for a while, takes a drink of water, and rests.

What did those words make you picture? _____

_____

What did you picture for...

1. him hammering? _____

2. the sparks? _____

3. him putting it back into the fire? _____

4. him resting? _____

4 **Seventh, Eighth, and Ninth Sentences:** Then he pulls the hot iron out again. With sweat pouring down his face, he hammers the metal flat. He repeats this for days until he has a fine hard blade for his sword.

What did those words make you picture? _____

_____

What did you picture for...

1. him pulling out the iron again? _____

_____

2. him sweating? _____

_____

3. the metal getting flatter? _____

_____

4. a fine blade? _____

_____

Picture Summary:

Number your images in order.

The sword smith pounds the softened metal ore with his hammer on the anvil, creating a shower of sparks.

The sword smith enters his dark hot smithy to make a sword out of iron.

The sword smith rests and then repeats the process for days.

The sword smith puts the iron into the blistering hot forge to soften it so that he can shape it.

Write a Word Summary:

_____

_____

_____

_____

_____

Critical Thinking

Main Idea:

Check the box that best describes all your images—the main idea.

☐ The sword smith softens iron in a hot forge and uses a hammer over and over again to shape it into a flat blade.

☐ The sword smith carefully takes the blistering hot iron out of the forge before he hammers it, creating a shower of sparks.

☐ The sword smith puts the sword in the hot forge with his tongs, so that he can soften it into a chunk of iron.

HOT Questions:

1. Do you think the sword smith's shop is hot while he's working? Why or why not? _____

_____

2. Why do you think he has to get the iron hot? _____

_____

3. Why do you think he uses tongs to remove the ore from the forge? _____

_____

4. Why do you think the iron glows orange? _____

_____

5. Why do you think there is a shower of sparks when he hammers? _____

_____

6. Why do you think he needs to rest and to drink water? _____

_____

7. Why do you think he flattens the iron? _____

_____

Make up an exciting story about something you might create in a smithy.

_____

_____

_____

_____

_____

_____

_____

_____

_____

_____

_____

_____

_____

_____

_____

_____

_____

_____

Did you use all of the Structure Words? Check each one you used.

☐ What   ☐ Number   ☐ Color   ☐ Mood   ☐ Background   ☐ Perspective
☐ Size   ☐ Shape   ☐ Movement   ☐ Where   ☐ When   ☐ Sound

19 Jacques Cousteau

Jacques Cousteau spent his life diving deep in the ocean to explore and study life there. Aboard his ship, the Calypso, he sailed all around the world exploring the seas. / He observed living creatures both in the water and on the sea bottom. To make this possible, he built an underwater breathing system that became scuba gear. / He discovered new things about how whales, sharks, and coral reefs live and thrive. He shared what he learned by writing books and making television shows for his eager fans.

Vocabulary to Visualize:

Jacques Cousteau: a famous underwater researcher who lived from 1910-1997
diving: going and staying under the water for a period of time
breathing system: a way to deliver air to a person who is underwater
scuba: a Self-Contained Underwater Breathing Apparatus made up of air tanks and a hose connected to a mouthpiece

---

1 **First and Second Sentences:** Jacques Cousteau spent his life diving deep in the ocean to explore and study life there. Aboard his ship, the Calypso, he sailed all around the world exploring the seas.

What did those words make you picture?_____

_____

What did you picture for...

1. Jacques Cousteau? _____

2. him diving?_____

3. Cousteau exploring the oceans? _____

4. the Calypso? _____

---

2 **Third and Fourth Sentences:** He observed living creatures both in the water and on the sea bottom. To make this possible, he built an underwater breathing system that became scuba gear.

What did those words make you picture?_____

_____

What did you picture for...

1. him observing? _____

2. the living creatures?_____

3. an underwater breathing system? _____

4. him using scuba gear? _____

3 **Fifth and Sixth Sentences:** He discovered new things about how whales, sharks, and coral reefs live and thrive. He shared what he learned by writing books and making television shows for his eager fans.
What did those words make you picture? _____

_____

What did you picture for...

1. Cousteau discovering new things? _____

_____

2. whales and sharks? _____

_____

3. coral reefs? _____

_____

4. him sharing what he learned? _____

_____

Picture Summary:

Number your images in order.

☐ Jacques Cousteau invented an underwater breathing system, which became scuba gear.

☐ Jacques Cousteau wrote books and made television shows about what he learned about sea life.

☐ Jacques Cousteau explored the world's oceans in his ship, the Calypso.

☐ Jacques Cousteau spent his life diving in oceans and observing living creatures he found there.

Write a Word Summary:

_____

_____

_____

_____

_____

_____

_____

Main Idea:

Check the box that best describes all your images—the main idea.

☐ Jacques Cousteau made television shows about his adventures sailing on the Calypso.

☐ Jacques Cousteau spent his time learning about life in the world's oceans and shared his findings through books and television.

☐ Jacques Cousteau invented an underwater breathing system so that he would no longer need to use his boat, the Calypso.

HOT Questions:

1. Why do you think Cousteau spent so much time in and on the water? _____

_____

2. Why do you think he invented the underwater breathing system? _____

_____

3. What do you think diving was like for Cousteau before he invented an underwater breathing system? _____

_____

4. Before Cousteau, do you think people could swim to the bottom of the sea? Explain. _____

_____

5. Why do you think he put his findings into books and television shows? _____

_____

6. Why might people want to hear about Cousteau's journeys? _____

_____

7. Do you think Cousteau's television shows were popular? Why or why not? _____

_____

Make up a story about an underwater diving adventure.

_____

_____

_____

_____

_____

_____

_____

_____

_____

_____

_____

_____

_____

_____

_____

_____

_____

_____

_____

Did you use all of the Structure Words? Check each one you used.

| ☐ What | ☐ Number | ☐ Color | ☐ Mood | ☐ Background | ☐ Perspective |
| ☐ Size | ☐ Shape | ☐ Movement | ☐ Where | ☐ When | ☐ Sound |

20 A Real Pirate Story

Pirates did not really lead exciting lives, fighting sea battles and stealing riches. Real pirate ships sailed for weeks alone on rough seas. / Most wooden pirate ships were small, with large sails and at least ten cannons. They could easily outrun and outgun large galleons loaded with cargo. / When there was no one to rob, the men would scrub the deck and clean the guns. The captain stocked grog so the men could drink and be happy when there was nothing to do. / The men smelled and their food was often rotten. Sleeping side by side in the tiny hold, they got in fights, even killing each other over silly things.

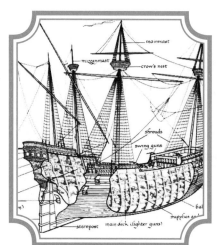

Vocabulary to Visualize:

pirate: a person who robs ships at sea
cannons: large guns used for firing heavy items like balls of metal
galleons: large sailing ships used from the 15th to 17th centuries
cargo: the contents or goods a ship carries
grog: an alcoholic drink
hold: the storage area of a ship

1 **First and Second Sentences:** Pirates did not really lead exciting lives, fighting sea battles and stealing riches. Real pirate ships sailed for weeks alone on rough seas.

What did those words make you picture? _____

_____

_____

What did you picture for...

1. pirates? _____

_____

2. sea battles? _____

_____

3. them stealing riches? _____

_____

4. rough seas? _____

2 **Third and Fourth Sentences:** Most wooden pirate ships were small, with large sails and at least ten cannons. They could easily outrun and outgun large galleons loaded with cargo.

What did those words make you picture? _____

_____

_____

What did you picture for...

1. the pirate ships? _____

_____

2. the sails of the ships? _____

_____

3. the cannons? _____

_____

4. the galleons? _____

3 **Fifth and Sixth Sentences:** When there was no one to rob, the men would scrub the deck and clean the guns. The captain stocked grog so the men could drink and be happy when there was nothing to do.

What did those words make you picture?_____

_____

What did you picture for...

1. the men scrubbing the deck? _____

_____

2. them cleaning the guns? _____

_____

3. the ship's captain? _____

_____

4. happy men? _____

_____

4 **Seventh and Eighth Sentences:** The men smelled and their food was often rotten. Sleeping side by side in the tiny hold, they got in fights, even killing each other over silly things.

What did those words make you picture?_____

_____

What did you picture for...

1. how the men smelled? _____

_____

2. their food?_____

_____

3. the hold where they slept? _____

_____

4. them fighting? _____

_____

Picture Summary:

Number your images in order.

☐ The pirates spent long periods of time sailing the rough seas without seeing another ship.

☐ The pirates slept in a tiny hold and often got into fights over silly things.

☐ The pirates scrubbed the deck and cleaned the guns when there were no ships to rob.

☐ The food was rotten, the pirates smelled, but the captain stocked plenty of grog to keep the men happy.

Write a Word Summary:

_____

_____

_____

_____

_____

Critical Thinking

Main Idea:

Check the box that best describes all your images—the main idea.

☐ Pirate life was full of outgunning and outrunning large galleons on the open seas, stealing their grog.

☐ Pirate life was not really exciting since it was difficult and uncomfortable for the sailors when there were no ships to rob.

☐ Pirate life was made up of long periods of time sailing without ever seeing another ship on the rough seas.

HOT Questions:

1. Why might people think a pirate's life was exciting? _____

_____

2. Why might it have been important for pirates to be able to outrun and outgun other ships? _____

_____

3. Why might it have been hard to find another ship on the open sea?_____

_____

4. Why do you think pirate captains wanted to keep their men happy?_____

_____

5. Why might it have been difficult to live on a pirate ship? _____

_____

6. Why do you think the pirates often smelled bad and ate rotten food? _____

_____

7. What silly things can you think of that the pirates might have fought over? _____

_____

Make up a scary story about a pirate adventure.

_____

_____

_____

_____

_____

_____

_____

_____

_____

_____

_____

_____

_____

_____

_____

_____

_____

_____

_____

Did you use all of the Structure Words? Check each one you used.

☐ What   ☐ Number   ☐ Color   ☐ Mood   ☐ Background   ☐ Perspective
☐ Size   ☐ Shape   ☐ Movement   ☐ Where   ☐ When   ☐ Sound

Notes

Analysis of Student Performance:

Notes

Analysis of Student Performance:

Notes

Analysis of Student Performance:

_____

_____

_____

_____

_____

_____

_____

_____

_____

_____

_____

_____

_____

_____

_____

Visualizing and Verbalizing® *Graded Workbooks* **Color Coding**

The colored checkers along the book's spine represent the grade level of the workbook. For example, the six orange checkers indicate that the workbook is written at a sixth grade reading level. The colored star helps differentiate between books a, b, and c in each workbook set.